The Blog of Blossom Street

RITA RAY

Illustrated by Susan Scott

OXFORD
UNIVERSITY PRESS

OXFORD
UNIVERSITY PRESS

Great Clarendon Street, Oxford OX2 6DP

Oxford University Press is a department of the University of Oxford.
It furthers the University's objective of excellence in research, scholarship,
and education by publishing worldwide in

Oxford   New York

Auckland   Cape Town   Dar es Salaam   Hong Kong   Karachi
Kuala Lumpur   Madrid   Melbourne   Mexico City   Nairobi
New Delhi   Shanghai   Taipei   Toronto

With offices in

Argentina   Austria   Brazil   Chile   Czech Republic   France   Greece
Guatemala   Hungary   Italy   Japan   Poland   Portugal   Singapore
South Korea   Switzerland   Thailand   Turkey   Ukraine   Vietnam

Oxford is a registered trade mark of Oxford University Press
in the UK and in certain other countries

British Library Cataloguing in Publication Data
Data available

ISBN 978-0-19-917957-2

19 20 18

Available in packs
Stage 10 Pack of 6:
ISBN 978-0-19-917954-1
Stage 10 Class Pack:
ISBN 978-0-19-917960-2
Guided Reading Cards also available:
ISBN 978-0-19-917962-6

Cover artwork by Susan Scott

Printed in China by Imago

Paper used in the production of this book is a natural,
recyclable product made from wood grown in sustainable forests.
The manufacturing process conforms to the environmental
regulations of the country of origin.

1

Snap was a small black and brown dog. He was the boss dog of Blossom Street.

One Saturday morning he walked up and down Blossom Street as usual.

He sniffed all the doorsteps and lampposts. He wagged his tail at all the children who saved scraps for him. He poked his head into baby Kelly's pram. Kelly laughed and touched Snap's wet nose.

Then Snap made sure that the dogs
and cats on the street were in their
places. Dogs had to stay in their own
back yards and cats had to sit on the
back yard walls. That's if they dared to
come out at all.

Snap trotted back to his own door.
Everything seemed fine on Blossom
Street. But everything was not fine.

Snap's owners, Ada and Harry, were
at home. This was odd. They always
went to work on Saturday mornings.
There were boxes everywhere. Harry
was taking a bed apart. Ada was
putting cups into a box.

'Hello, Snap,' she said, as he came in.

Snap sniffed the boxes. 'You'd better have your Doggy Chunks before the van comes.'

'What van?' Snap thought. He soon found out. A big van came to the front of the house. Two men helped Harry and Ada to put all their things in the van.

'I can't move away!' thought Snap.
'Who's going to look after Blossom
Street? Who will play with the children
and keep the other dogs off the street?
Who will make sure the cats stay on
the back yard walls?'

'Come on, Snap,' called Harry. 'Say
goodbye to Blossom Street.' He picked
Snap up and put him in the front of
the van.

The children on Blossom Street came out to wave as the van set off. Kelly's mum gave Snap a bit of cake.

As he looked out of the van window Snap thought, 'If I move away, how can I do my job? I'm the boss dog of Blossom Street, but I can't stay behind. I can't leave Ada and Harry. Dogs stay with their owners. Not like some cats I know. They'll go anywhere for a warm fire.'

2

The van had to go slowly all the way to the new house. There was a big orange bus in front of it. Snap watched the bus and it gave him an idea. By the time he got to the new house he had a plan.

The plan could help him to be boss dog of Blossom Street, even if he didn't live there any more.

Snap felt a bit happier when he jumped out of the van. He went to sniff every corner of his new home.

The next day was Sunday and Ada and Harry had to unpack things. The new house had a garden at the back instead of a yard.

'The dogs round here stay in their own gardens,' Ada told Snap. 'There's no strutting about being boss dog. I'll take you for a walk later.'

Snap went to see what was at the end of the garden and he heard a yapping sound. Something was trying to get through the fence. It was a little Yorkie dog with a red ribbon tied in a bow on top of its head.

Snap couldn't believe it. 'Ugh!' he thought. 'What a wimp! That's not a *real* dog! They wouldn't have a dog like that on Blossom Street.'

He didn't even bother to bark at the little dog. He heard its owner call, 'Foofoo, Foofoo pie! Come to Mummy.'

'Yuk!' thought Snap. 'Let me get back to Blossom Street.'

On Monday morning Harry and Ada went to work. 'I've left a key next door,' said Ada to Snap. 'Foofoo's owner will let you out in the garden, and we'll be home at five o'clock.'

'Will you stop talking to that dog as if he understands?' said Harry.

'What do you mean? Of course he understands, don't you, Snap?' said Ada.

Later, Foofoo's owner unlocked the door into the garden.

'Good,' thought Snap.

He ran into the garden and started to dig a hole.

'Bad doggie,' called Foofoo's owner. 'Don't teach my little Foofoo bad tricks.'

Snap tried to talk to the dog on the other side. He was a large bulldog with droopy eyes.

'This looks better,' thought Snap. He barked in a friendly way. But the big dog said nothing at all.

'I can't stand this much longer,' thought Snap. 'I must try to get back to Blossom Street.'

That night he fell asleep thinking of
his plan for keeping his eye on Blossom
Street. As soon as Harry and Ada had
driven off in their car the next day,
Snap started to work on his plan.
Opening doors was easy for a clever
dog like Snap.

He set off down the path and out of the front gate. He stopped at the bus stop and stood near a man and a woman.

When the big orange bus came he jumped on behind them so that the bus driver didn't notice him. He sat up at the back and watched out of the window.

Soon they came to Blossom Street
and Snap got off behind a man with a
shopping bag. The driver just saw his
tail disappearing.

'Whose dog is that?' he shouted.
'Has anybody paid for him?' But it was
too late.

3

Snap was already running down Blossom Street. He sniffed at all the doorsteps and the lampposts. He chased a cat back on to the yard wall.

He put his head into Kelly's pram. Kelly laughed so much that her mum looked to see what was happening.

'Snap!' she cried in surprise. 'What
are you doing here?' Snap wagged his
tail and looked hungry.

'Come inside,' said Kelly's mum.
'There's some meat left from yesterday.
You can eat that.'

When the children came home
from school they yelled, 'Snap! Snap!
We thought you'd gone for ever.'
They patted him and hugged him.
He played with them until they were
called in for tea.

'It's five o'clock,' said Kelly's mum. 'I'd better take Snap back to his new house.' She went to the door and called, 'Snap! Snap!' but Snap was not there. The children looked up and down Blossom Street. But they could not see him. In the end, Kelly's mum set off to Snap's new house.

Ada and Harry were glad to see
Kelly's mum. 'Hello, Irene. It's nice of
you to visit us,' they said.

'I've come about Snap. Oh, he's here!'

'Of course he's here,' said Ada.
'He lives here. He was fast asleep in the
kitchen when we came home. I think
he likes his new home.'

'Then why was he in Blossom Street all day? I came to tell you,' said Kelly's mum.

'Blossom Street? How could he be? It must be a dog that looks like him,' said Harry.

'Oh no, it was Snap all right. Ask the children.'

'Just come in the other room a minute,' Ada whispered. 'Snap understands every word, you know.'

'Rubbish!' said Harry, but he went into the other room to hear Ada's plan.

'I've got a day off tomorrow,' said Ada. 'I'll pretend to go to work as usual but I'll hide and see what he does.'

Next day Ada watched Snap get on
the big orange bus. She wanted to
laugh. 'What a clever dog!' she
thought. 'He does understand.'

She went to Blossom Street and
watched Snap from Kelly's mum's
front room.

At half past four Snap trotted off to the bus stop and caught the bus home. The bus driver said, 'It's you again, is it?' and let him on without paying.

When Ada and Harry got home Snap was curled up, fast asleep. 'No wonder you feel tired,' said Ada. 'It's hard work looking after Blossom Street all day.'

Snap pricked up his ears and opened one eye. 'We know all about it, Snap.'

Just then there was a knock on the front door.

'It's a reporter from *The Daily Snoop*,' said Harry. 'He wants a photo of Snap. The bus driver told him about a clever dog who rides on the bus by himself. More like a naughty dog, I think.'

Snap jumped up and wagged his tail. He liked having his photo taken. The next day everyone in Blossom Street saw him on the front page. The headline said, *Snap goes by Bus!* Lots of people came to ride on the bus with Snap so the bus driver made plenty of money. And Snap is still the boss dog of Blossom Street, even though he doesn't live there any more.

About the author

My name is Rita Ray. I think
it is a good name for a writer
because people find it easy
to remember.

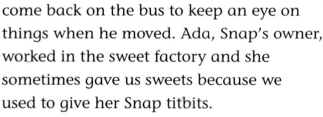

Snap the dog lived in our
street when I was a child.
He was the boss dog of
our street and he really did
come back on the bus to keep an eye on
things when he moved. Ada, Snap's owner,
worked in the sweet factory and she
sometimes gave us sweets because we
used to give her Snap titbits.